Piano Exam Pieces

ABRSM Grade 7

Selected from the 2015 & 2016 syllabus

Name

Date of exam

C000171928

Contents

Editor for ABRSM: Richard Jones

Other pieces for Grade 7

First published in 2014 by ABRSM (Publishing) Ltd, a wholly owned subsidiary of ABRSM, 24 Portland Place, London W1B 1LU, United Kingdom © 2014 by The Associated Board of the Royal Schools of Music

Music origination by Julia Bovee Cover by Kate Benjamin & Andy Potts Printed in England by Headley Brothers Ltd, The Invicta Press, Ashford, Kent.

MIX Paper from responsible sources FSC™ C109619

A:1

Fugue in A minor

M. I. Glinka
(1804–57)

Con moto [♩ = c.96]

The Russian composer Mikhail Ivanovich Glinka studied piano with John Field in St Petersburg. He conceived the notion of creating an indigenous Russian national music and exerted a profound influence on later Russian composers, including Tchaikovsky, Prokofiev and Stravinsky. In 1833–4 Glinka studied counterpoint and composition in Berlin with Siegfried Dehn, of whom he reported: 'He had the student practise writing three- and four-voice fugues, which hastened the development of his taste and brought order to his theoretical understanding of music.' The Fugue in A minor 'a 3 voci con 2 soggetti' dates from 1834 and is thus a direct product of Dehn's tuition.

The two subjects, both built on a chromatic descent through a 4th, are combined at the outset (bb. 1–4). After the opening exposition (bb. 1–17), the second subject is presented in a more elaborate version (bb. 21–35; see the bass of bb. 22–4). A lengthy development (bb. 36–62) is devoted to the first subject only, which is first inverted (bb. 36–9), then treated in stretto (overlapping entries; bb. 40–52). In the coda that follows the climactic pause chord on the dominant (b. 62), there are no further subject entries, only motivic allusions. The composer's dynamic markings are restricted to incidental hairpins till b. 58. Thus overall dynamics are largely left to the player's discretion. 'Adagio' in b. 72 should be taken in its old sense of *allargando*.

Source: *Fuga a 3 voci con 2 soggetti* (St. Petersburg: Th. Stellowsky, c.1865).

Sonatina in D minor

HWV 581

A:2

G. F. Handel
(1685–1759)

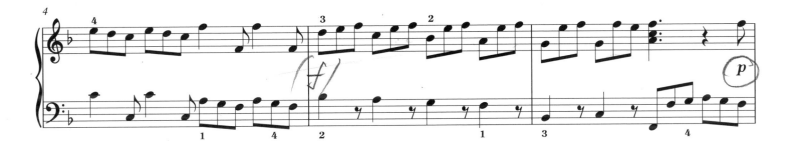

This Sonatina is thought to be one of Handel's earliest keyboard pieces, perhaps composed around 1705 when he was only 20 and living in the north German city of Hamburg. There he played violin, and later harpsichord, in the Hamburg opera. At that time, too, he composed keyboard pieces, arias, cantatas, and his first opera *Almira*.

   The Sonatina originally acted as finale to the early Suite in D minor, HWV 437. Accordingly, it is written in the time and rhythm of a gigue – the customary ending of a suite – though it is not cast in the usual binary dance form. Instead, it falls into four sections, each opening with the theme (at bb. 1, 11, 26 and 35) – an elementary type of ritornello form as cultivated by the early Italian concerto writers Torelli and Albinoni. The echo at b. 6 invites an echo-dynamic scheme such as that suggested by the editor.

Sources: MS copies, London, British Library, Add. MSS 31573 and 31577

© 1984 by The Associated Board of the Royal Schools of Music

Adapted from Handel: *Selected Keyboard Works*, Book II, edited by Richard Jones (ABRSM)

Allegro

First movement from Sonata in G, K. 283

A:3

W. A. Mozart
(1756–91)

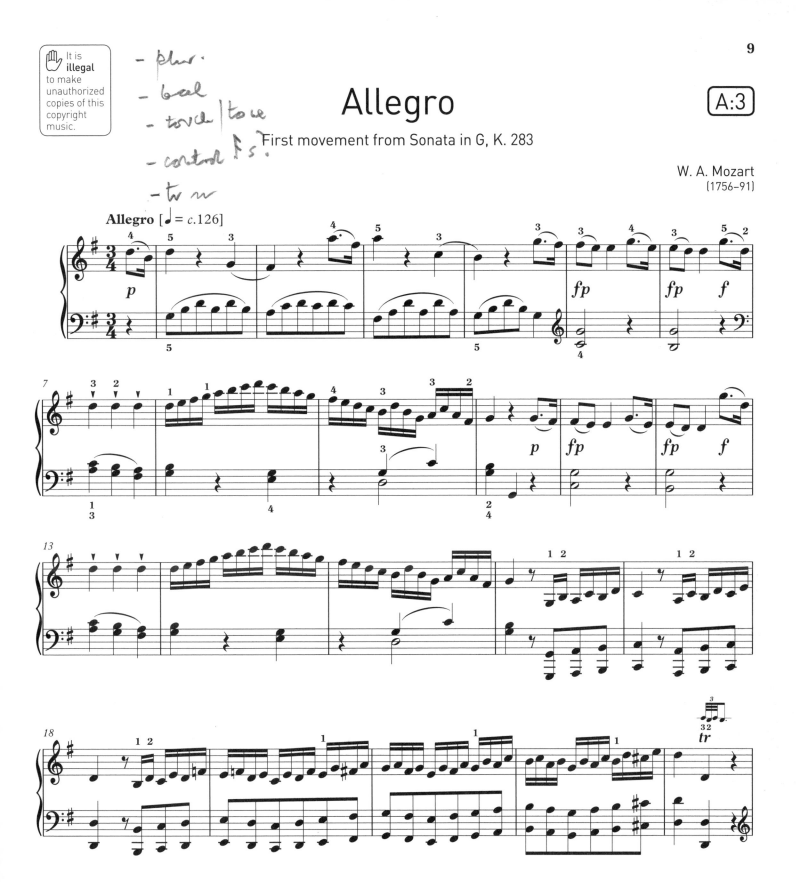

The Sonata in G, K. 283, from which this Allegro has been selected, is the fifth of a set of six piano sonatas – Mozart's earliest contributions to the genre, written at the age of 19 while he was staying in Munich in early 1775. The set might have been intended for publication, but only one of the six was published during Mozart's lifetime. In 1777 he wrote to his father from Augsburg: 'Here and at Munich I have played all my six sonatas [in public] by heart several times.'

The first subject of this Allegro is notable for its gentle, graceful beauty – relatively rare at the start of a sonata-form first movement. By contrast, the second subject (b. 23) is characterized by syncopation and Scotch snaps. The subsidiary theme that follows (b. 31) is dramatic, with its strong *piano/forte* and staccato/legato contrasts. There is no real development, but rather a brief episode (b. 54) that introduces a couple of ideas not heard elsewhere. Mozart compensates by developing his first subject at the start of the recapitulation (bb. 72–82). According to Denis Matthews in his performance notes to the ABRSM edition, 'The tempo is that of a lively but still graceful minuet.'

Source: autograph MS (formerly in Staatsbibliothek zu Berlin, Preussischer Kulturbesitz)

© 1978 by The Associated Board of the Royal Schools of Music
Adapted from Mozart: *Sonatas for Pianoforte*, Vol. I, edited by Stanley Sadie (ABRSM)

水草舞
Third movement from 美人鱼组曲

Shui Cao Wu

Third movement from *Mei Ren Yu zu qu*

Mingxin Du
(born 1928)

Shui Cao Wu The Dance of Watergrass; **Mei Ren Yu zu qu** The Mermaid Suite

The Chinese composer Mingxin Du studied at the Yucai School in Chongqing. In 1948 he moved to Shanghai, where he performed as a solo pianist. He taught at the Tchaikovsky Music Conservatory in Moscow from 1954 to 1958, and later joined the staff of the Central Conservatory in Beijing.

'The Dance of Watergrass' is a neo-Romantic tone-picture, written in an essentially conservative tonal idiom. An eight-bar introduction leads to a ternary structure with modified reprise (ABA[1]). Section A (b. 9) is notable for its spread chords and for the tonic-major/minor contrast that eventually permeates the whole piece. The *tranquillo* middle section, with its simple, folk-like melody, is largely in the tonic minor. The reprise of A (b. 51) is free: only the tonic-major bars (bb. 17–28) return exactly, after which the tonic minor takes over in a free further discourse on the main theme, incorporating allusions to the *tranquillo*.

18

B:2

By a Meadow Brook

No. 9 from *Woodland Sketches*, Op. 51

Edward MacDowell
(1860–1908)

The American composer Edward MacDowell studied in France and Germany, receiving encouragement from Liszt, who was impressed by some of his compositions. He returned to America in 1888, working as a teacher and composer in Boston till 1896, when he was appointed professor of music at Columbia University.

   MacDowell's *Woodland Sketches*, Op. 51, from which this piece is selected, were one of the last fruits of his Boston period. They were composed in 1896, published in the same year, and the collection soon became one of his most popular works. 'By a Meadow Brook' is a lyrical, programmatic piece in tripartite form (ABA¹). Section A, which returns at b. 33, is warmly expressive in its harmony, culminating in the 'Tristan' chord (b. 15; from the opening theme of Wagner's *Tristan und Isolde*). Section B (b. 17) is very different, strongly resembling a certain playful mood of Grieg's. Although the composer's metronome mark is ♩. = 63, candidates may prefer a more relaxed tempo, for example ♩. = *c*.52. Either tempo would be acceptable in the exam.

Source: *Woodland Sketches*, Op. 51 (Boston: P. L. Jung, 1896)

Kevätyö

No. 4 from *Toukokuu*, Op. 27

B:3

Selim Palmgren
(1878–1951)

Kevätyö Night in May; **Toukokuu** May

Selim Palmgren was a Finnish contemporary of Sibelius. He studied piano and composition at the Helsinki Conservatory from 1895 to 1899. Later he travelled to Germany and Italy, pursuing advanced studies with, among others, Busoni. During the 1920s he toured the USA and taught at the Eastman School of Music in Rochester, New York. From 1936 till his death in 1951 he was professor of harmony and composition at the Sibelius Academy in Helsinki. His compositions include 5 piano concertos, about 200 songs, and approximately 300 lyrical piano pieces.

This piece is selected from Palmgren's *Toukokuu*, Op. 27, a collection of seven piano pieces composed in 1906–7 and first published in 1912. 'Kevätyö' (literally 'Spring Night') is a powerfully evocative piece in a late Romantic idiom. The composer here utilizes to the full his impressively rich harmonic palette. The thematic material is laid out in bb. 1–11, developed in bb. 12–26, then briefly recapitulated at the end (bb. 27–35).

Source: *Night in May/Kevätyö* (London: Augener, 1916)

Carousel

Sylvie Bodorová
(born 1954)

The Czech composer Sylvie Bodorová studied in Bratislava and at the Janáček Academy of Performing Arts in Brno, where she later taught. She was composer-in-residence at the University of Cincinnati, Ohio in 1994–6.

Carousel, composed in Prague in 2000, is a brilliant toccata whose character is determined by the idea of a merry-go-round. The quaver figures can be taken to represent the carousel's speed of movement; the chordal theme (bb. 6–11), the sheer joy of its ride; and the almost obsessive return of the same themes, its constant rotation. The middle section (bb. 40–56) is based on a quaver figure first introduced in b. 32. The main theme of the opening section (b. 6) returns at b. 57 to round off the piece. No metronome mark is given, since the instruction 'As fast as possible' speaks for itself. The concluding *glissando* is to be played by the right hand, on the white keys and in free time.

Selected from *Spectrum 3, an international collection of 25 pieces for solo piano*, compiled by Thalia Myers (ABRSM)

- quiet colour
- tempo grado.
- balance
- Chords
- connecting
- ped

Canope

No. 10 from *Préludes*, Book 2

C:2

Claude Debussy
(1862–1918)

Très calme et doucement triste [♩ = c.60]
[Very calm and sweetly sad]

mouvt
[in time]

Claude Debussy, perhaps the most influential French composer of modern times, studied piano, theory and composition at the Paris Conservatoire from 1872 to 1884. As winner of the *Prix de Rome*, a much coveted composition prize, he travelled to Rome and stayed there from 1885 to 1887. He often toured Europe, England and Russia, performing his own music as conductor and pianist. Debussy's mature piano music is regarded by many as the most original contribution to the repertory since Chopin. In his short piano pieces, the music is typically linked to visual impressions, though this element is downplayed in the *Préludes* by placing the title in brackets at the end of each piece. The *Préludes*, arranged in two volumes of 12 pieces each, are among Debussy's most mature compositions, dating from 1909–10 (Book 1) and 1911–13 (Book 2).

The title 'Canope' refers to a city in ancient Egypt that gave its name to Canopic jars – urns used for holding the entrails of embalmed bodies in ancient Egyptian burials. Debussy kept two such jars on his desk. A sense of mystery and antiquity is conveyed by the modal harmony and the parallel common chords. The piece unfolds freely, as often in Debussy, though there is a clear element of reprise at b. 26.

Source: *Préludes, Livre II* (Paris: Durand, 1913)

animez un peu
[speed up slightly]

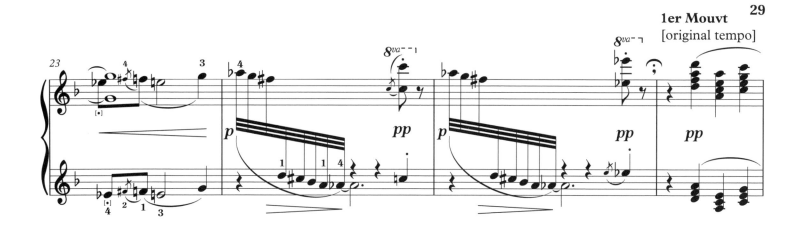

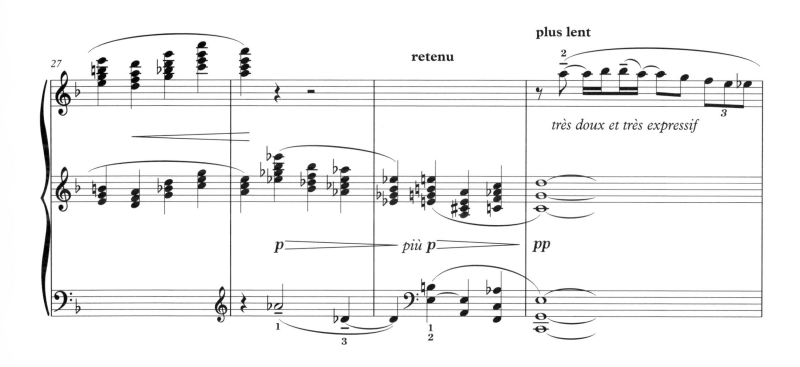

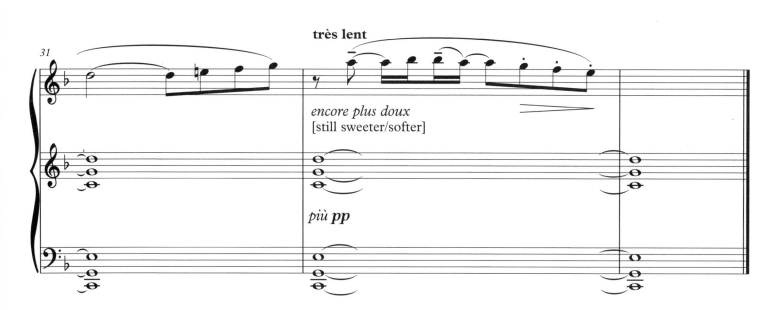

C:3

Prelude in D flat

No. 15 from 24 Preludes, Op. 34

Dmitry Shostakovich
(1906–75)

Dmitry Shostakovich, the foremost Russian composer of the Soviet era, learnt the piano as a child from his mother, who was a professional pianist. As a young man, he achieved success as a pianist as well as a composer, representing his country at the first International Chopin Piano Competition in Warsaw in 1927. By then he had already composed his first piano pieces, which are written for the instrument with great skill.

The 24 Preludes, Op. 34, were composed in 1932–3, first performed by the composer himself in Moscow in May 1933, and published in 1935. Like Shostakovich's later 24 Preludes and Fugues, Op. 87, they may be regarded as a tribute to Bach, for both collections imitate *The Well-Tempered Clavier* by including a piece (or a pair of movements in Op. 87) in all the keys. Whereas Bach's key order is chromatic, however, Shostakovich's is cyclical, ascending through the entire circle of fifths. It has been reported that Shostakovich thought of the Op. 34 preludes as a series of psychological sketches. The state of mind illustrated in the Prelude in D flat, a dance-like scherzo, seems to be a certain grim humour that often haunts the Russian composer's music – here, lighter at the beginning and end but darkening more and more in the middle. Although the composer's metronome mark is ♩. = 76, students may prefer a tempo of ♩. = c.69. Either tempo would be acceptable in the exam.